Busy People
All Around Town

By R. W. Alley

MERRIGOLD PRESS • NEW YORK

It is dawn at the airport, and already airplanes are taking off and landing. The Express Mail plane is just in with rush letters and packages from places far away.

Ralph the deliveryman picks up a big load. He must hurry to deliver packages all over the city. He's never been late.

Usually Ralph's dog, Max, helps. But today Max doesn't help. "Oh, no!" shouts Ralph. "There goes one of my packages!"

BEEP! BEEP! HONK! HONK!

The highway into the city is crowded. Everyone is in a rush to get to work, but no one is moving.

Tracy the traffic reporter, up in her helicopter, knows why. "An accident at the toll plaza looks like trouble for commuters."

On Oak Farm people are already at work. The cows need milking. The pigs need feeding. And look at all the eggs the hens have laid!

Ralph wonders, "Where did Max go?"

There is a detour ahead—more problems for drivers!
Ralph turns right. Dibbs Diner is jammed for breakfast. Clara the cook really needs her new toaster. "Thanks, Ralph!" she says.
"How about a hot chocolate to go," says Ralph.

At the lumberyard Larry cuts wood into boards of all sizes. He can really use that new blade.

The trash collectors are just coming back with the city's trash. They have been working since sunrise. But they haven't seen Ralph's missing package.

WHIR! RACHITTY! CLUNK!

The factory machines are just starting up. Some factories make things to eat. Some factories make things to wear. Big factories often make small things, and small factories often make big things.

Ralph delivers packages to all of them. "Here's a special rush order, Mr. Boomer," says Ralph. But he doesn't see Max anywhere.

At the railroad yard big boxcars are being loaded. Ed the engineer will push them together to make a long train. "Thanks for the new cap, Ralph," he shouts.

"It looks good," Ralph calls back.

The road is full of trucks taking goods from the factories to the city. Their drivers are in a hurry, just like Ralph. But everyone has to wait while a coal barge goes under the drawbridge, heading for the power plant.

Sick people come to the hospital to get well. Some need operations. Others need special medicine.

"Here are some X rays, Doctor Molloy," says Ralph.

Desmond the dentist gets new false teeth for Mrs. Jones.

A patient gets flowers. "Hope you feel better," says Ralph, smiling.

Nurse Nora tells Ralph, "I have not seen your dog because no dogs are allowed."

All day long truckloads of food come to the grocery store.
Frank makes sure the frozen things stay frozen.
Prudence weighs the fresh farm produce.
Egbert checks the eggs.
Candy stacks the soup and coffee, but not too high.
Delbert slices the deli meat out front, while Butch cuts steaks in the back.

And Grace the grocer keeps track of everything. She can tell by the smell that Ralph's fish delivery is fresh. But she can't tell about Max. "The only dogs I've seen today are hot dogs."

Gus can fix any car at his garage, if he has the right part. Ralph brings him the parts he needs.

"This carburetor fits just fine," says Gus as he tightens it in place with his special tools. Gus is quite a mechanic. He is always busy.

"Could you tune up my van next week, Gus?" asks Ralph.

"Sure," says Gus.

Gus's daughter, Doris, sells new cars.

It looks like Martin will need a new car. Even Gus can't fix that wreck!

BANG! BANG! CHUG! CHUG! CLOP! CLOP!

The construction site is very noisy. Men rivet together the outside frame and hammer together the inside walls. A crane lifts up the pipes and ducts. Masons mix mortar to hold the bricks together. But where do the windows go? The foreman needs the new blueprints to show him. "Just in time, Ralph!" he says.

"Glad to help," shouts Ralph.

WHHHAAAAA! WHHHAAAAA!

That's the firehouse alarm! The fire fighters rush to their trucks and off they go.

It's time for lunch—but not at Betty's Burgers! "It all started in the fry bin," Betty tells the TV reporter.

The fire fighters spray foam on the flames in the kitchen. Outside, the fire trucks pump water from the hydrants up and out through the hoses. The fire fighters get as close to the fire as they dare and douse it thoroughly. At last it's out.

Everything is all wet, but Rose doesn't mind. Her plants were looking a little dry.

Ralph is glad he brought his own sandwich. He brought lunch for Max, too. But where is that dog?

RRRRRIIIINNNGGG!

Recess is over. It's time to go back to class.

In the science lab everyone is working on their projects for the Science Fair.

In geography class students learn about faraway places.

Tommy is taking trumpet lessons in the music room.

Coach is trying to teach his class about badminton in the gym.

And in the library, where it is quiet so people can read, Ralph delivers the new encyclopedia—not so quietly.

"Sorry," whispers Ralph.

Dexter's downtown department store is very crowded, as usual. The shoppers know that Dexter will have almost anything they need. He even has things they didn't know they needed. And new things are being delivered to all the floors all the time.

Escalators and elevators take the shoppers up and down. Lots of shoppers go down to the Bargain Basement, where everything is cheap.

Ralph is thinking about getting a new tie. He asks the salesclerk, "Which do you like better?"

Down Plummet Street is Dimple's Deli, where people go for the best sandwiches in the city.

Peas Hill Arcade is across the street. There are many small shops here, and Ralph makes lots of deliveries.

Manny fixes violins and teaches Violet to play.

Ernest sews in seams and hems. He has fine fabric for suits, too. "Maybe I should get a new suit for my tie," says Ralph.

Louise styles hair.

Joe fixes old and worn shoes, and Barbara sells brand-new ones. "Of course, new shoes would be more useful," thinks Ralph.

Ralph has no delivery for Paula's pet shop today. "But where did this extra pup come from?" wonders Paula.

At City Hall, Mayor Mel is making a speech. He is telling everyone to vote. Norman the reporter takes notes for the newspaper.

Inside, Clem the clerk is getting another phone line. Now he will be able to talk to two people at once!

Judge Brown's courtroom is packed. The judge must decide who caused the accident.

Sergeant Sam gets a call at the police station.

Someone zips by on a rooftop. It's Max!

Ralph shouts, "There he goes!"

BONG! BONG! BOINK! Bink! Dink.

Felix is fixing the city clock. He really needs the part Ralph delivers. "I hope this will fix the chime," says Ralph.

At five o'clock many people stop their work and get busy doing other things.

Some have chores to do. Laura goes to the laundry. Marvin mows the grass.

Other people take classes. Jack helps people build muscles. Fritz shows his students how to paint pictures.

Still others go to the park. Salty rents out boats for the river. A brass band plays marches in the bandstand. The Little League has an important game.

Who's that stealing third base?

As the sky begins to get dark some people are just starting their workday.

In restaurants chefs are cooking, and waiters and waitresses are setting tables and serving meals.

Hotel Filbert is busy, too. People check into rooms. Bellhops carry their bags. Maids make sure there are clean sheets and towels. Is that Max trying to check in?

At the newspaper office the evening edition is being printed. Norman's story is on the front page. Other reporters will work all night to write stories for the morning edition.

Ralph wonders if he should put in an advertisement for a lost dog and a missing package.

After dinner there is still a lot to do in town.
The City Players are putting on a new play.
Bob's bowling alley is having a tournament.
It's bingo night at the social hall.
People wait in line at the Fine Arts Cinema to see the movie
Ralph has just delivered. Thelma threads the film carefully in
the projector. "Sorry you can't stay for the show."
"Tell me if it's good," answers Ralph.
At the Music Fair the concert has begun. Though all the seats
are filled, people around the city can hear the concert on
the radio.

It is night now.

Almost everyone goes home to sleep. The Smiths go home to a house with a big yard. The Fishers go home to a town house without a yard. The Roberts go home to an apartment in a tall building where many families live.

Ralph's van is empty now. He goes home, too. His home is on wheels. "I guess that package is lost and late. I hope I will never be late again!"

Who's that on the stoop? It's Max with the package!

"It's so good to have you back!" Ralph hugs Max and looks at the label. "It's for ME!"